Hansel & Gretel

Retold and Illustrated by John Patience

Once upon a time there were two children named Hansel and Gretel who lived with their parents on the edge of a great forest. Their father was a Woodcutter who worked very hard, but even so, the family was very poor.

PUBLISHED BY PETER HADDOCK LTD
BRIDLINGTON ENGLAND
© PETER HADDOCK LTD
Printed in Italy
ISBN 0 7105 0342 3

One day, the Woodcutter's wife said to him, "Husband, we have no money left and there is not enough food in the larder to feed us all. There is only one thing to do. You must take the children deep into the forest and leave them there, or we shall all starve."

Unknown to their parents, Hansel and Gretel had overheard the conversation. "Don't worry," whispered Hansel to his sister, "I have thought of a plan to save us."

The next morning their mother gave Hansel and Gretel a crust of bread each and told them to save it for lunch. Then sadly she waved them goodbye.

The poor Woodcutter led his children into the forest.
But as he walked, Hansel crumbled up his bread to leave
a trail of breadcrumbs, so that he and his sister could
find their way back home.

At last, deep in the forest, they stopped. The Wood-cutter told his children to gather some sticks and build a fire. When the fire was burning brightly, he said, "Now children, wait for me here. I am going off to chop wood. When I have finished I will come back for you." But the Woodcutter did not come back. As the children sat by the fire it grew darker and darker and the sounds of wild animals began to fill the forest.

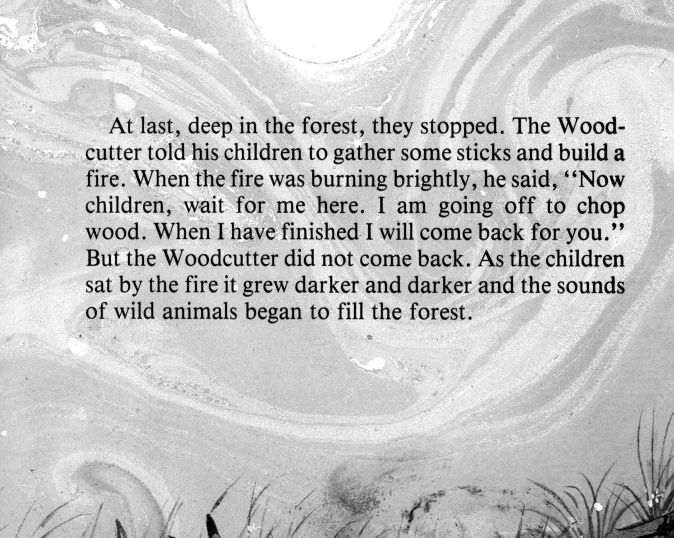

Hansel and Gretel huddled together to comfort each
other until, eventually, they both fell asleep. When they
awoke the next morning, the children were eager to
follow Hansel's trail of breadcrumbs back home, but
the birds in the forest had seen Hansel laying the trail
and had swooped down and eaten up all the crumbs.

"Never mind," said Gretel bravely. "Follow me. I shall soon have us home again." And so the two children set off through the forest. On and on they walked, but they were hopelessly lost and felt very hungry. They were beginning to think they might die of

hunger in the forest, when they came upon a snow white dove, singing on the branch of a tree.

The bird spread its wings and flew on a little way ahead of them. ''It wants us to follow,'' cried Hansel.

They followed the dove until it arrived at a cottage and perched on the roof. It was the most extraordinary cottage they had ever seen! It was made of candy, cake, marzipan and barley sugar, and the windows were of clear spun sugar!

The children ran up to the house and the poor things were so hungry that they broke off pieces and ate them. Suddenly the door opened and a little old woman came out. "Ah, you poor children," she exclaimed. "You look very hungry." "We are," replied Gretel. "We are lost and have not had any food since yesterday."

So the old woman took the children inside and gave them all kinds of good things to eat and drink. The

cottage was as bright and clean as a new pin and the old lady had three fluffy white cats for pets. After they had eaten, the children were tired, so the old woman tucked them up in two little beds. "Sleep well," she said, "I will call you when it is time for breakfast."

But the old woman, who was really a wicked witch, came into the room in the night, and pulled Hansel out of bed. She locked him in a cage and said, "When you are fat I shall have you for my dinner!" The witch gave Hansel all the best and most fattening things to eat, but Gretel, who was made to do all the housework, was given only dry crusts to eat. The witch's house had been under a spell to make it look nice; now it appeared as it really was – dirty and untidy. As for the three fluffy white cats, they had turned into horrible, hissing, spiky, black things.

Every morning the old witch came to the cage and said, "Hansel, stretch out your finger so that I may feel whether you are getting fat." But Hansel used to stretch out a bone, and the old woman, who had very bad eyesight, thought it was his finger and wondered why he did not get fatter.

Finally, the witch decided she could not wait any longer for Hansel to get fat, and that she would eat him straight away, thin though he was. "I am going to bake some bread," said the crafty old woman to Gretel. "See if the oven is hot enough." Gretel replied, "I do not know how to do that. Our oven at home was different."

"You stupid child," cried the angry witch. "I'll show you. Watch me." And she opened the oven door. In an instant Gretel raced across the room and pushed the wicked witch inside and locked the door.

Then she let Hansel out of his cage. "Now we must search the house. I'm sure that the witch must have treasure hidden somewhere," said Hansel. And sure enough, the children found a great chest full of gold and precious stones. Gretel filled her apron with treasure and Hansel took a gold casket which he filled with jewels. Then they set off to find their way back home.

After walking for some time through the forest, the children came to a wide river. "I don't think we can get across," said Gretel. "We have no boat. What shall we do?" Close to the bank a large swan was gliding by. "Please help us," begged Hansel. The swan came to the bank. "Sit on my back," it said. "I will carry you safely across." The swan carried Hansel over the river and then went back for Gretel.

After thanking the swan, Hansel and Gretel went on a little way through a part of the forest which seemed to grow more and more familiar to them. At last, they saw their own house and at the door were their mother and father. The Woodcutter and his wife were overjoyed to see their children again, and welcomed them back with open arms. The treasure made them rich and they never went hungry again. And they all lived happily ever after.